Top Gear

VRROOOMM!

BBC Children's Books
Published by the Penguin Group
Penguin Books Ltd. 80 Strand, London WC2R 0RL,
England
Penguin Group (Australia) Ltd, 250 Camberwell Road,
Camberwell, Victoria 3124, Australia (a division of
Pearson Australia Group Pty Ltd)
Canada, India, New Zealand, South Africa

Published by BBC Children's Books, 2008
Text and design © Children's Character Books, 2008

10 9 8 7 6 5 4 3 2 1

Written by David Carr
Designed by Dan Newman

BBC and Top Gear (word marks and logos) are
trademarks of the British Broadcasting Corporation
and used under license.
Top Gear © 2005
BBC Logo TM & © BBC 1996.

ISBN: 978-1-40590-453-7

Printed by Clays Ltd.

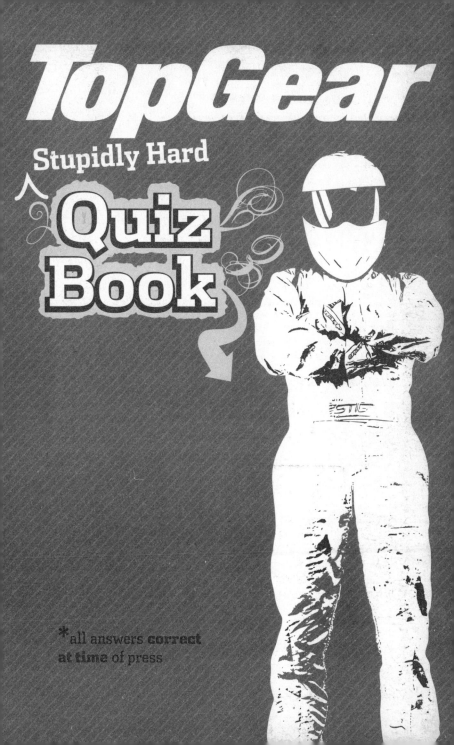

TopGear

Stupidly Hard

Quiz
Book

*all answers **correct**
at time of press

Contents

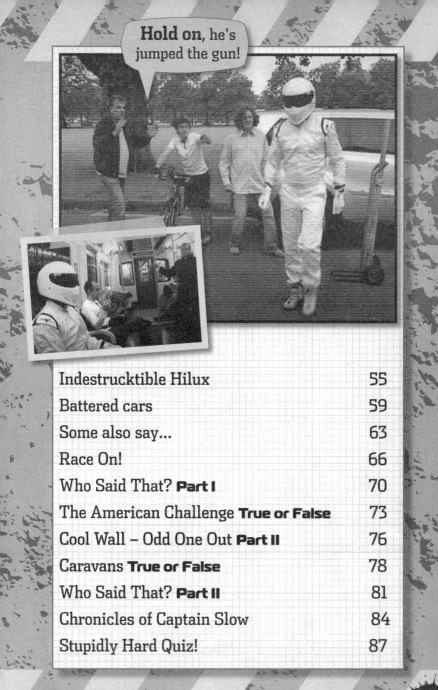

Hold on, he's jumped the gun!

Could you be The Stig?

If the time came for a new tame racing driver to be crowned, would you have the nerve, the skill and the fear of ducks to become The Stig? Take the test and find out!

1. The colour of the next Stig would be:

a) Red
b) Blue
c) Neon Green
d) Silver

2. You're driving an Ascari A10 at approximately 120mph on the test track when, on your approach to Hammerhead, a rear tyre blows, sending you into an uncontrollable spin. What do you do?

a) Start screaming and signal to emergency crews to call an ambulance.
b) Get a firm grip on the steering wheel and do your best to control the vehicle, hoping you don't hit the tyre wall.
c) Turn up the stereo so you can hear your favourite song over the revving engine.
d) Take the opportunity to get a quick nap in and let the Ascari do its own thing.

3. If you were to have a household pet to keep you company, what would it be?

a) A cat named James
b) A hamster named Richard
c) A house plant named Steve
d) A dog named Jeremy

4. Given the choice of listening to whatever you wanted while taking a lap in an Ariel Atom (if it actually had a radio), would you play...

a) 'Guilty' by Barbra Streisand & Barry Gibb
b) *Spanish For Beginners* by Alfredo Cruz
c) Nothing
d) Classical baroque

5. Where would you take your holidays while Top Gear is off the air?

a) Isle of Capri, Italy
b) Silverstone, Northamptonshire
c) Majorca, Spain
d) The Bahamas

6. What sort of car would you drive in your leisure time?

a) What leisure time?
b) Take my pick from the Top Gear garage
c) Pagani Zonda F
d) Ford Focus RS

7. The Stig has an unknown number of relatives around the world. We've already met two of them, in the USA and Botswana. Where do you expect the next member of the Family Stig to pop up?

a) Australia: Dame Edna Everstig
b) Tibet: Dalai Stigma
c) Japan: Takashi Stig-san
d) France: Pepe Le Stig

8. Everyone knows The Stig has a tattoo of Buzz Aldrin on his thigh. What kind of tattoo would you get to prove your Stigness?

a) The Renault logo on your bicep
b) A flaming skull with Maserati MC12s jumping out of each eye socket across your back
c) 'Colin' above your right nipple after the founder of Lotus, Colin Chapman
d) A teddy bear with its head resting on your belly button

9. On October 26 each year, do you...

a) Do a spot of housework then watch your 'Best of Le Mans' DVD

b) Observe the anniversary of the signing of the Treaty of Ripon between Scotland and England in 1640

c) Celebrate the National Day of Austria

d) Enjoy your birthday with friends

10. Which past Grand Prix champion should a Stig try to emulate?

a) Nigel Mansell

b) Lewis Hamilton

c) Damon Hill

d) None of the above

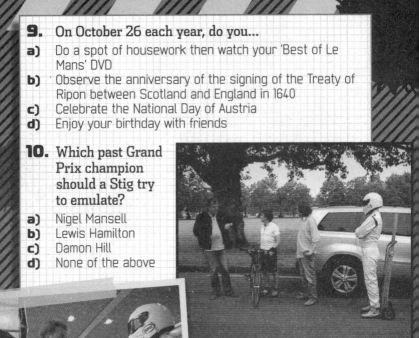

Answers

1. **a)** or **d)** Either of these would be acceptable, not to mention completely cool.

2. **c)** The Stig doesn't scream, pray or sleep.

3. **c)** Obviously.

4. **c)** Nothing. The Ariel Atom doesn't have a stereo.

5. **b)** The Stig is sentimental.

6. **b)** Obviously.

7. Any of these is possible.

8. **b)** I think we can agree the others are seriously uncool.

9. **d)** Er, that would be d.

10. **d)** The Stig? Emulate a Grand Prix driver? Please!

Scores

8-10: You must have 98 RON petrol running through your veins. You sure you're not related?

4-7: There's no doubt, you're ice cold. A little more time on the track, a little less chat and it's unleash The Stig!

0-3: Sorry, but the closest you're going to get to The Stig is the poster of him on your bedroom wall. Come on, you know you've got one.

Testing Times

The test track is the spiritual home of Top Gear. The place where reputations are made and records are broken. Keep a close eye on the clock for this challenge, but be careful – there's some tricky turns thrown in just for you.

1. How long is the Top Gear test track?
a) 1.5 miles (2.41 kilometres)
b) 2 miles (3.2 kilometres)
c) 2.5 miles (4 kilometres)
d) 3 miles (4.8 kilometres)

2. Where is the test track located?
a) Stigton Common
b) Salisbury Plain
c) Dunsfold Park
d) Wuthering Heights

3. What type of shape is it?
a) S-Bend
b) Figure-8
c) U-Turn
d) Wide Loop

4. How many turns are there?
a) 6
b) 12
c) 8
d) 9

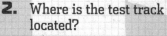

RRMMMBLL

5. What make of vehicle has done the most number of laps on the test track?

a) Koenigsegg
b) Ferrari
c) Suzuki
d) Volkswagen

6. Which of the following is not a section of the Top Gear test track?

a) Hammerhead
b) Baltimore
c) Chicago
d) Bentley

7. Engineers from which British car manufacturer designed the test track?

a) Jaguar
b) Lotus
c) Rover
d) Noble

8. Which British actor had a corner named in his honour after almost rolling the Suzuki Liana he was driving?

a) Neil Morrissey
b) Steve Coogan
c) Alan Davies
d) Michael Gambon

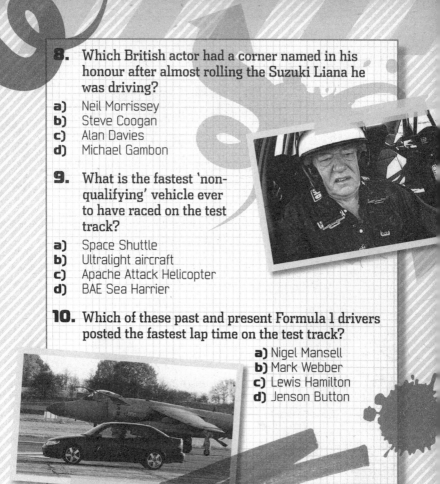

9. What is the fastest 'non-qualifying' vehicle ever to have raced on the test track?

a) Space Shuttle
b) Ultralight aircraft
c) Apache Attack Helicopter
d) BAE Sea Harrier

10. Which of these past and present Formula 1 drivers posted the fastest lap time on the test track?

a) Nigel Mansell
b) Mark Webber
c) Lewis Hamilton
d) Jenson Button

Answers

1. **b)** 2 miles (3.2 kilometres)
2. **c)** Dunsfold Park (Surrey).
3. **b)** Figure-8
4. **d)** 9.
5. **c)** Suzuki (Liana, the Reasonably-Priced Car driven by Stars).
6. **b)** Battimore.
7. **b)** Lotus.
8. **d)** Michael Gambon.
9. **d)** BAE Sea Harrier.
10. **a)** Nigel Mansell (1:44.4).

Scores

8-10: Be interesting to see your time in a reasonably-priced car.

4-7: A fairly good knowledge of the twists and turns. Pity you forgot about the tyre wall.

0-3: Let's just say you wouldn't be allowed on the track in a caravan!

Challenged!
True or False

Though obviously not as demanding as the big ones, mini challenges still present a tantalising opportunity for the lads to show off their skills at crashing, sinking and making a general mess. Exercise your grey matter with these 10 questions.

1. The team decided that the best driving road in the world is from Davos in Switzerland to the Stelvio Pass in Italy.

TRUE / FALSE

2. In a challenge to drive an amphibious vehicle across the English Channel, Richard's Volkswagen Vanagon or 'Damper van' was the only successful competitor.

TRUE / FALSE

3. A Bugatti Veyron is faster over two miles than a Eurofighter Typhoon.

TRUE / FALSE

4. In The race across London challenge, the team discovered the fastest way to get across London was by bicycle.

TRUE / FALSE

BBLLBBLBBLLBLBLBLBLBLLBBRRI

5. In The British Leyland challenge, James' Austin Princess came out on top and £20 in the black.

TRUE / FALSE

6. Competing in the Britcar 24 hour endurance race at Silverstone, the team finished in last place out of 59 competitors.

TRUE / FALSE

7. Jeremy, Richard and James proved it is possible to resurface a road in 24 hours.

TRUE / FALSE

8. James took the Bugatti Veyron to its top speed of 253mph at a test track in Germany.

TRUE / FALSE

9. James and Richard failed to convert a Triumph Dolomite into a space shuttle in the required amount of time.

TRUE / FALSE

10. James builds a limousine out of a Saab and a Citroen, with the interior as half a Swedish sauna and half a French café.

TRUE / FALSE

BLAM BLAM BLAM

Answers

1. *True.*
2. *False. The team made the trip in two seconds.*
3. *False. The Typhoon is faster by Jeremy's Nissank.*
4. *True. Ridden by Richard.*
5. *True.*
6. *False. They did rather well, all things considered, coming in 39th and third in their class.*
7. *True.*
8. *Amazing but True.*
9. *False. The car was a Reliant Robin and it successfully took off before crashing into a nearby hillside.*
10. *False. The cars were a Saab and Alfa Romeo. Half sauna, half Sistine Chapel.*

Scores

8-10: *It's a little scary how much you know about half-baked experiments involving cars. Keep up the good work!*

4-7: *Nice one. Expect a phone call the next time the lads are looking to do something really stupid.*

0-3: *You need to lighten up and unleash your inner boffin.*

Cool Wall – Odd One Out
Part I

The source of many heated arguments between Jeremy and Richard, the Cool Wall gives them the opportunity to voice their opinions on the 'coolest' and 'uncoolest' cars on offer. Now you have a chance to do the same. Pick out the odd car in the following lists. Hope you know your stuff...

1. Dodge Caliber, Honda Civic, Volvo C30, Porsche 911

2. Fiat 500, Smart ForTwo, Mercedes C-Class, Volkswagen EOS

3. Citroen C4 Picasso, Land Rover Freelander, Volvo C30, Toyota Prius

4. Vauxhall Tigra, Peugeot 207 CC, Nissan Qashqai, Dodge Caliber

5. Aston Martin V8 Vantage, Audi TT, Honda Civic, Porsche 911

6. Cadillac XLR, BMW 1-Series, Mitsubishi Evo 9, Toyota Auris

7. Lamborghini Gallardo, Ferrari P3, Mercedes CLS, Alfa Romeo Brera

8. Audi A8, Noble MI5, Mazda RX8, Volkswagen Phaeton

9. Lexus LS, Vauxhall Astra Twintop, Volkswagen Beetle, Ferrari Enzo

10. Morgan Aero 8, Vauxhall Monaro, Pagani Zonda, Lotus Exige

Answers

1. **Dodge Caliber** (Seriously Uncool, the others are Cool)
2. **Fiat 500** (Sub-Zero, the others are Uncool)
3. **Toyota Prius** (Seriously Uncool, the others are Cool)
4. **Nissan Qashqai** (Uncool, the others are Seriously Uncool)
5. **Aston Martin V8 Vantage** (Subzero, the others are Cool)
6. **BMW 1-Series** (Seriously Uncool, the others are Uncool)
7. **Ferrari P3** (Cool, the others are Sub-Zero)
8. **Volkswagen Phaeton** (Sub-Zero, the others are Cool)
9. **Volkswagen Beetle** (Seriously Uncool, the others are Uncool)
10. **Morgan Aero 8** (Uncool, the others are Sub-Zero)

Scores

8-10: Simply Sub-Zero

4-7: Kinda cool, but also kinda uncool. Does that make you lukewarm?

0-3: Sorry, but you're destined to drive a Volkswagen Beetle for eternity.

Stars in Reasonably-Priced Cars

Glittering international celebrities they may be, but out on the Top Gear test track our Stars in Reasonably-Priced Cars are mere putty in the hands of The Stig; whose task it is to turn them into hardened racing machines. It works – sometimes. See if you can score better than many of our visiting celebs in this quick quiz...

1. Who was the first ever celebrity guest on Top Gear, appearing in Episode 1 on 20 October, 2002?

a) Neil Morrissey
b) Joanna Lumley
c) David Soul
d) Harry Enfield

2. Two different makes of car have been driven by celebrities around the Top Gear test track, the Suzuki Liana and Chevrolet Lacetti. Who is the fastest in each car?

----

3. How many females are in the top ten on the Lacetti leader board?

a) 1
b) 2
c) 3
d) 4

4. How many celebrity chefs have driven around the test track?

a) 1
b) 2
c) 3
d) 4

SCREEEECH!

KRUMMP

5. What did Jeremy call the section of the board with lap times slower than 1:50, noted for its large number of actors and comedians?

a) Off Broadway
b) The Cheap Seats
c) The Dead Zone
d) The Thespian Zone

6. Which of the following descriptions is not an official Top Gear test track condition?

a) Very Wet
b) Mildly moist
c) Oily
d) Hot

7. How many seconds does a Very Wet track add on to a driver's lap time?

a) 2 seconds
b) 4 seconds
c) 8 seconds
d) None of the above

8. Who played Obi-Wan Kenobi in the Star Wars movies and posted a time of 1:48.0 in the Lacetti?

----

9. How many Doctor Whos have completed lap times in a Reasonably-Priced Car?

a) 1
b) 2
c) 3
d) None

10. Several football players have tested their driving skills on the track. Name two of them.

Winter Olympics Special

True or False

For something entirely different, the producers decided to send the team to Norway for a series of Winter Olympic-sized challenges in and around Lillehammer. They figured the cold might slow them down a bit. It didn't. Question is, how slow are you going to be getting through these teasers?

1. Jeremy challenged James to a cross country driving and shooting biathlon, the loser of which had to eat 'golden snow'.

TRUE / FALSE

> I **don't** want to **eat golden snow!**

2. James was the one who had to eat the golden snow.

TRUE / FALSE

3. Jeremy raced a Jaguar XK8 against a speed skater on an ice course and won by three seconds.

TRUE / FALSE

4. James again beat Jeremy, this time in a race on a frozen lake.

TRUE / FALSE

5. Jeremy lost when the Jaguar he was driving spun off into a snow bank and got stuck.

TRUE / FALSE

VRROOOMM

6. Richard took on James in a race between a bobsleigh and a rally car. Richard was in the rally car and terrified.

TRUE / FALSE

7. The bobsleigh again took the checkered flag, by three seconds.

TRUE / FALSE

8. In a game of five-a-side hockey, ten Ford Mondeos knocked a puck around the ice.

TRUE / FALSE

9. Miraculously, with a little help from Jeremy, James' team won the match.

TRUE / FALSE

I've won a Top Gear challenge!

10. With some assistance from the United Kingdom Rocketry Association, the team strapped rockets to the back of a local Norwegian car and sent it down a ski-jump, in an attempt to beat the distance set by a ski-jumper.

TRUE / FALSE

Answers

1. True
2. False. Incredibly, James won. And somehow, Jeremy avoided the unpleasant task.
3. False. With no grip on the surface, Jeremy was lapped twice and easily beaten.
4. True
5. True
6. False. He rode the bobsleigh.
7. True
8. False. The cars were Suzuki Swifts.
9. False. Richard's team won 5-4.
10. False. They strapped the rockets to the back of a Mini.

Scores

8-10: Nice one, Sven. Clearly you've spent a bit of time in the Nordic regions.

4-7: If this were the alpine decathlon you'd be on track for a bronze. Oh dear.

0-3: Sorry, but it's the yellow snow for you, friend.

Just Jeremy

True or False

When you're dealing with someone like Jeremy Clarkson, a man known around the world for his love of brash statements, spotting the falsehoods in this lot is going to be tough indeed. Good luck!

1. In the first amphibious vehicle challenge, Jeremy renames his Nissan, 'Nissank'.

TRUE / FALSE

2. He proved that it is possible to drive a Volkswagen Golf up a Scottish mountain.

TRUE / FALSE

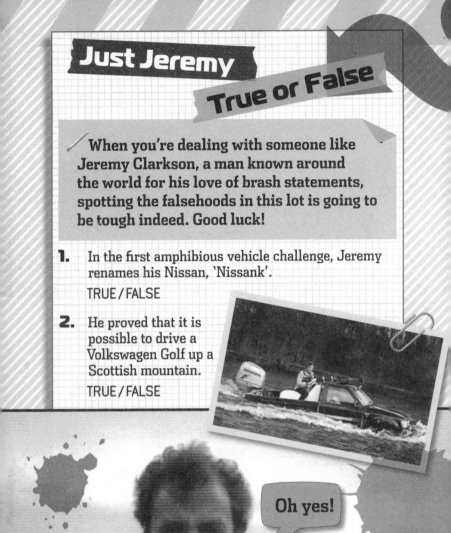

Oh yes!

KA-POWWW

3. Jeremy loved the Ford GT so much he drove it around the Top Gear track until it ran out of petrol.

TRUE / FALSE

4. In the race across London during rush hour traffic, Jeremy rode in the back of a taxi.

TRUE / FALSE

5. Jeremy's ultimate crush is Keira Knightley.
TRUE / FALSE

6. Jeremy was so smitten with Ms Scott-Thomas when she appeared on the show that he wore a tuxedo.
TRUE / FALSE

7. Jeremy's idea of a stretch limousine is to create a 70 metre version of a Ford Mondeo.
TRUE / FALSE

8. Jeremy completed so many circles in the Prodrive P2 that he made himself throw up.
TRUE / FALSE

Oh, hang on....

EEEEEYOOWWWW

9. He managed to outmanoeuvre an Apache Attack chopper.

TRUE / FALSE

10. And in a simulated battle with a Challenger 2 tank, he also survived unscathed.

TRUE / FALSE

Answers

1. *False. This was the name of his vehicle in the second challenge.*
2. *False. The car was a Land Rover Discovery.*
3. *True.*
4. *False. He drove a powerboat up the Thames.*
5. *False. Close but that honour would have to go to Kristin Scott Thomas.*
6. *False. A suit perhaps, but nothing as flash as a tux.*
7. *False. He stretched a Fiat Panda.*
8. *True. It wasn't pretty.*
9. *True. For a while. Before it locked its guns on him.*
10. *False.*

Scores

8-10: *Your knowledge of Clarkson is spot on. And you're just like him. Always right!*

4-7: *Given how predictable the man is, it's surprising you didn't do better.*

0-3: *As Jeremy would say. 'It's all gone horribly wrong!'*

... he is confused by stairs and that his brain is a satellite navigation system. Who can be sure? But while his personal life may be a mystery, there are some very public things we know about Colonel Fotherington Digby-Stigby. What do you know?

1. According to Jeremy, what disorder does The Stig suffer from?

a) Webbered Feet
b) Jenson's Buttocks
c) Mansell Syndrome
d) Hamilton Hands

2. How did The Black Stig perish, causing the creation of The White Stig?

a) He drank biofuel
b) He drove off an aircraft carrier
c) His head was crushed in a freak electric sunroof accident
c) He lives!

3. Which Formula 1 racing driver was presented with a T-shirt that stated 'I Am The Stig'?

a) Mark Webber
b) Jenson Button
c) Nigel Mansell
d) Lewis Hamilton

4. What did The Stig drive down a ski jump in Lillehammer, Norway?

a) Rocket-powered Mini
b) Rocket-powered James May
c) Three-speed bicycle
d) Snowmobile

5. The Stig has family in many other countries around the world. Name two of these countries, featured on the show.

_____

6. Complete the following. "Some say he once punched..."

a) a Land Rover Discovery
b) a hole in the ozone layer
c) a horse to the ground
d) his own shadow

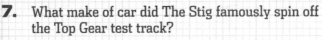

7. What make of car did The Stig famously spin off the Top Gear test track?

a) Koenigsegg CCX
b) Pagani Zonda F
c) Noble M15
d) All of the above

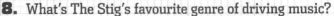

CRASH

8. What's The Stig's favourite genre of driving music?

a) Prog rock
b) Power ballads
c) Baroque
d) All of the above

9. What car was The Stig driving when he was pulled over by Scottish police officers?

a) Aston Martin DBS
b) Ascari KZ1
c) TVR Sagaris
d) Caterham Seven

10. Who is The Stig?

a) Gordon Brown
b) Richard Hammond
c) Madonna
d) Don't ask stupid questions

Answers

1. c) Mansell Syndrome
2. b) He drove off an aircraft carrier
3. a) Mark Webber
4. d) Snowmobile
5. Botswana and the USA
6. c) a horse to the ground
7. a) Koenigsegg CCX
8. d) All of the above
9. d) Caterham Seven kit car
10. d) Don't ask stupid questions

Scores

8-10: (Silence. You have pleased The Stig)

4-7: Perhaps you're not as Stig-like as you think you are.

0-3: The last time The Stig was upset he came to grief on an aircraft carrier. Do you really want to upset him again?

How Hard Can It Be?
True or False

Mostly impossible. But if you think that's going to prevent Jeremy, Richard and James from attempting some of the most hair-brained challenges ever seen on television, think again.

1. A convertible people carrier can successfully travel at 100mph without losing its canvas roof.

TRUE / FALSE

2. And it will, if a Top Gear presenter has anything to do with it, cause a fire in a car wash.

TRUE / FALSE

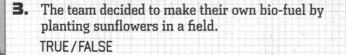

3. The team decided to make their own bio-fuel by planting sunflowers in a field.

TRUE / FALSE

4. In a race to the Magnetic North Pole, Richard, on a sled being pulled by ten Inuit dogs, narrowly defeated Jeremy and James in a Hilux.

TRUE / FALSE

VRROOOMM

5. Using the bio-fuel from their crop, the team competed in a 24-hour endurance race, finishing last place.

TRUE / FALSE

6. According to professors at the Scottish National Gallery of Modern Art the Alfa Romeo Brera is the best-looking coupé on the road.

TRUE / FALSE

7. In a race against the Audi TT and Mazda RX-8, it's also the fastest.

TRUE / FALSE

8. Jeremy completed a lap of the infamous Nürburgring in under 10 minutes.

TRUE / FALSE

9. German former motor racing driver Sabine Schmitz later beat Jeremy's time in a Ford Transit van.

TRUE / FALSE

10. Jeremy, Richard and James are guaranteed lucrative careers as drive time radio presenters.

TRUE / FALSE

Top Gear
Highway Code

Anyone wishing to drive on British roads must first complete a theory test, covering general rules, road safety, hazards, signage and more. However, when the Top Gear team cast an eye over the contents, they noticed some glaring omissions. So, in order to provide a more rounded overview of what to expect when out on the road, they put together the Top Gear Highway Code Questionnaire; an essential document designed to fill the gaps missing from the so-called 'official' version. See how you go with the following questions...

1. The maximum speed you can drive on a UK motorway when towing a caravan is 60mph. What is the maximum speed you can drive when attempting to jump five caravans in a Volvo 240 Estate?

a) 60 mph
b) 70 mph
c) None of the above. A Volvo 240 Estate would never go that fast.

2. In the diagram below, the amphibious 'Damper van' is looking to make a left turn at the roundabout. The Triumph Herald 'sailboat' however, coming from the opposite direction, wants to turn right. Which driver's hairstyle is bigger than their vehicles?

a) The short bloke in the 'Damper van'.
b) The guy in the 'sailboat' with the big hair.
c) They both have ridiculously big hair.

3. What is the curb to curb turning circle of a Fiat Panda stretch limo?

a) 50 feet
b) 150 feet
c) Cannot answer since it hasn't finished turning

4. Imagine you are driving the high-performance Maserati MC12 supercar, when you come across a 'toucan crossing'. How is a 'toucan crossing' different from other crossings?

a) Cyclists can use it
b) There is a flashing light
c) They are manned by toucans

SKREEEEEEEEEEEE

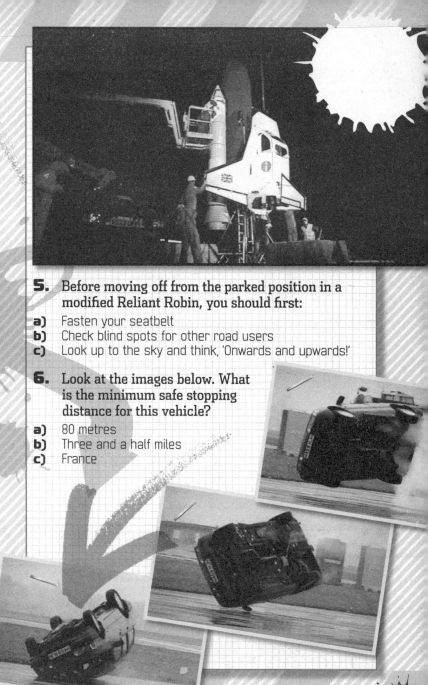

5. Before moving off from the parked position in a modified Reliant Robin, you should first:

a) Fasten your seatbelt
b) Check blind spots for other road users
c) Look up to the sky and think, 'Onwards and upwards!'

6. Look at the images below. What is the minimum safe stopping distance for this vehicle?

a) 80 metres
b) Three and a half miles
c) France

7. Choose the most appropriate outcome in this situation:

a) The driver allows the pedestrian to cross safely before moving on.

b) The driver hails the pedestrian and gives him a map for a different city, thus confusing the pedestrian and allowing the driver to win the race.

c) The pedestrian, aware that the car is being driven by an ultra-competitive television presenter, allows the driver to move on then calls a taxi.

8. Before overtaking in Iceland you should always:

a) Signal to the other vehicle by creating an impressive arc of water with the rear of your car.

b) Pass at a safe speed, but fast enough so as to avoid sinking.

c) Check your blind spot for marine mammals.

VARROOOMMM

9. In the image below, circle which objects are in the driver's blind spot:

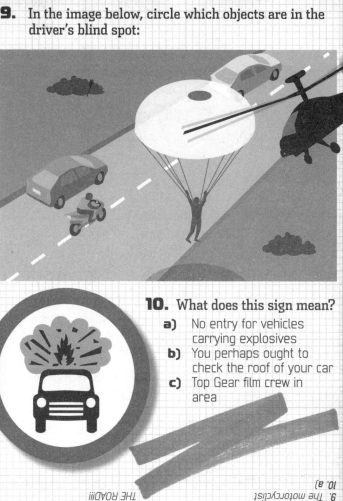

10. What does this sign mean?

a) No entry for vehicles carrying explosives

b) You perhaps ought to check the roof of your car

c) Top Gear film crew in area

Answers

1. c)
2. c)
3. c)
4. a)
5. c)
6. a)
7. Any answer is suitable
8. b)
9. The motorcyclist
10. a)

Scores

7-10: PASS. Thanks to your preparedness the streets will be a safer place when you finally get your license.

4-6: NEAR PASS. Don't worry, you'll get there eventually!

0-3: FAIL. Please, for the sake of your fellow citizens. STAY OFF THE ROAD!!!

The African Challenge

True or False

The drive across Botswana was one of the lads' most challenging motoring treks and proved to be a gruelling test of second-hand vehicles and a little trying for the Top Gear team. Which of these survived? Who won the race? And will the lads ever be able to get the dust out of their clothing? Test your memory of the challenge with these questions.

1. Jeremy chose a Mercedes Benz 230E for the trek across Botswana.
TRUE / FALSE

2. Richard named his car Oliver.
TRUE / FALSE

3. If any of the three vehicles chosen by the lads broke down along the journey, the driver would be forced to complete the trip in a Volvo 760.
TRUE / FALSE

4. The Makgadikgadi is a massive stretch of land with a surface composed mostly of salt.

TRUE / FALSE

5. In order to defend himself from the ferocious creatures of the Okavango Delta, Jeremy used leftover cardboard boxes to cover the passenger-side door of his car.

TRUE / FALSE

6. After crossing a river, Jeremy and James drained the water from their cars using a bucket and hose.

TRUE / FALSE

7. The lads' journey was across a part of Botswana known as the 'spine of Africa'.

TRUE / FALSE

8. Richard left a cow's head in James' tent, only to realise later that it was his own tent.

TRUE / FALSE

9. The lads enlisted the help of the Deputy Prime Minister of Botswana to test drive their safari vehicles.

TRUE / FALSE

10. The border of Botswana and South Africa signalled the end of the African challenge.

TRUE / FALSE

Supercar Parts

So you think you know your Ferrari from your Maserati? Take a close look at these supercars and see if you can guess the right model.

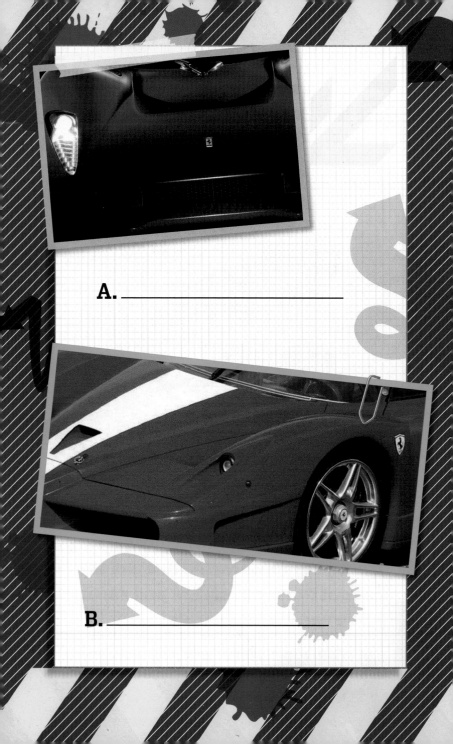

A. _____

B. _____

I don't think I'll **ever, ever** get out of it!

C. _____

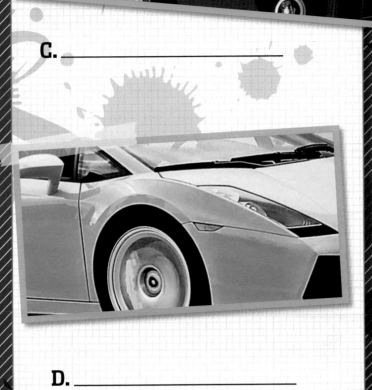

D. _____

E. _____

It is a **huge**, giant **leap forward**... it is an engineering **hammer blow!**

F. _____

G. _____

H. _____

I. _____

It's like pressing a **button** on a beautifully crafted **watch**... and all the **volcanoes** in the world **erupt!**

J. _____

K. _____

It's like putting a Saturn V **rocket** in a food blender!

L. _____

Answers

Power Lappin'

Our tame racing driver has run many a supercar through its paces on the track. Now it's your turn to put your memory to the test with these 10 Power Lap posers.

1. Which of the following cars is not in the top ten of the Top Gear Power Board?

a) Ferrari 599 GTB Fiorano
b) Lamborghini Murciélago LP640
c) Ariel Atom 2 300
d) Pagani Zonda F

2. Two makes of car have two cars in the top ten. Can you name them?

a) Porsche and Ferrari
b) Ferrari and Koenigsegg
c) Koenigsegg and Ascari
d) Ascari and Porsche

3. What is currently sitting in last place on the Power Board?

a) Aston Martin DB5
b) Bowler Wildcat
c) Ford Mondeo ST220
d) Subaru Impreza WRX Sti

4. Can you guess how many Lamborghinis are on the Power Board?

a) 4   **b)** 5
c) 7   **d)** 9

5. Which country designs and manufactures the Koenigsegg?

a) Denmark   **b)** Czech Republic
c) Italy   **d)** Sweden

6. Which car is in first place on the Power Board?

a) Pagani Zonda F
b) Maserati MC12
c) Ascari A10
d) Lamborghini Murcielago

7. What does the 'F' stand for in Pagani Zonda F?
a) Fast
b) Fabulous
c) Fangio
d) Ferrari-chaser

8. Which car in the top ten has a lot of speed but not a lot of body work?

a) Mercedes McLaren   b) Ariel Atom
c) Porsche Carrera GT   d) Noble M15

9. Which of these makes of car has never made it onto the Power Board?

a) Toyota   b) Mazda
c) Cadillac d) Bentley

10. Which car has appeared the most on the Power Board?
a) Ferrari
b) Mercedes
c) Lamborghini
d) Porsche

Answers

1. a) Ferrari 599 GTB Fiorano (it currently sits in 12th position)
2. c) Koenigsegg and Ascari
3. a) Aston Martin DB5
4. b) 5
5. d) Sweden
6. c) Ascari A10
7. c) Fangio. After the legendary racing champion, Juan Manuel Fangio.
8. b) Ariel Atom
9. a) Toyota
10. d) Porsche (nine times)

Scores

8-10: Fantastic. The Ferrari Enzo of quiz scores!
4-7: Not bad. Perhaps the awesome speeds made you dizzy.
0-3: OK, so they're quick, but pay attention!

51

Hamster Tales

True or False

Always up for a race against his fellow hosts, Richard is the go-to guy of the team when a theory needs to be put to the test. Or is he? Try your hand at these true or false teasers.

1. In a drag race against Jeremy in an Audi R8, Richard, in his own Porsche 911 Carrera 2S, lost by 3.1 seconds.

TRUE / FALSE

2. In the African Challenge, Richard's Opel Kadett was the only car to not shed any weight for the drive across the Makgadikgadi salt pan.

TRUE / FALSE

3. Richard revealed he tried to have the Opel shipped over to the UK but British Customs would not allow it.

TRUE / FALSE

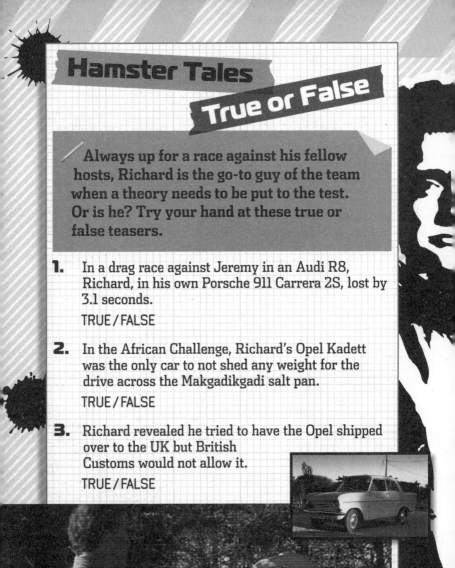

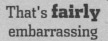

That's **fairly** embarrassing

4. Richard won the 'Worst Dressed Presenter Award' for 2007 for wearing bicycle shorts in the Race Across London.

TRUE / FALSE

5. Richard Hammond's great grandfather invented the Hammond organ.

TRUE / FALSE

6. When Richard tried to add a Ducati 1098 motorcycle to the Cool Wall, Jeremy removed it with a chainsaw.

TRUE / FALSE

7. Given the task of stopping the rocket-powered mini at the end of the Lillehammer ski-jump, Richard placed the barrier on the wrong run.

TRUE / FALSE

ARRRGGH!

8. Richard got his nickname 'Hamster', after it was revealed he used to race the furry creatures as a child.

TRUE / FALSE

9. Richard has never won the Nobel Prize for Really Excellent Challenges.

TRUE / FALSE

10. In a fight with Jeremy over the placement of the BMW M6 on the Cool Wall, Richard ate the picture of the car.

TRUE / FALSE

Answers

1. *False. The slow-motion replay revealed Richard's Porsche beat Jeremy in the Audi.*
2. *True.*
3. *False. Richard successfully adopted Oliver the Opel, who now sits proudly in one of his many garages.*
4. *False. Jeremy beat him with his drysuit.*
5. *False. Of course not!*
6. *True. Jeremy doesn't like motorcycles.*
7. *True. Sad but true.*
8. *False.*
9. *True.*
10. *True. Hamsters eat cardboard.*

Scores

8-10: *Spookily good. Is your name Richard?*

4-7: *The thing is, how can you be sure your answers were wrong?*

0-3: *A poor effort. True or true?*

54

Indestrucktible Hilux

The trusty red Toyota Hilux withstood test after test put to it and now sits proudly aloft in the Top Gear studio. How many metal-crunching moments from the destructive challenge can you recall?

1. In which city did Jeremy begin his systematic destruction of the Toyota Hilux pick-up truck?

a) Norwich
b) Bristol
c) Oxford
d) Manchester

2. What was the first test he put the big red truck through?

a) He ran it into a tree
b) He hit it with a spade
c) He drove it down a flight of stairs
d) He called it a sissy

3. What did Jeremy then drive the Hilux into, causing environmentalists to phone in and complain; not to mention cause distress among the yokels?

a) A statue
b) A tree
c) A caravan
d) A park bench

4. Jeremy decided a good drowning would do the trick and chose which famous waterway to dowse the Hilux?

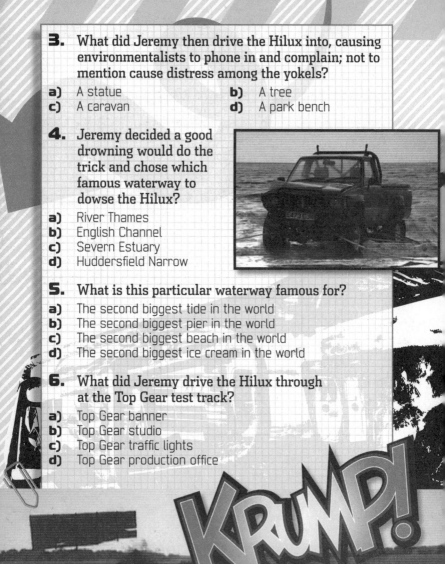

a) River Thames
b) English Channel
c) Severn Estuary
d) Huddersfield Narrow

5. What is this particular waterway famous for?

a) The second biggest tide in the world
b) The second biggest pier in the world
c) The second biggest beach in the world
d) The second biggest ice cream in the world

6. What did Jeremy drive the Hilux through at the Top Gear test track?

a) Top Gear banner
b) Top Gear studio
c) Top Gear traffic lights
d) Top Gear production office

KRUMP!

E473 CJN

7. And then he dropped this unfortunate object onto the Hilux...

a) A caravan
b) Richard Hammond
c) A Volvo
d) A Swede

8. When Jeremy retired defeated, James took over and decided to place the Hilux on top of what?

a) A waterbed
b) A caravan
c) A high-rise building
d) A cliff

9. And do what to it?

a) Drop it from a great height
b) Sink it
c) Roll it
d) Buy it a drink

10. Miraculously, the Hilux survived every attempt to destroy it, proving that all you need to keep the mighty pick-up going is a basic toolkit and a can of ____?

a) Tuna
b) WD-40
c) UB-40
d) Oil

CHUG CHUGGA BRRRMMM

Answers

1. b) Bristol
2. c) He drove it down a flight of stairs
3. b) A tree
4. c) Severn Estuary
5. a) The second biggest tide in the world
6. d) Top Gear production office
7. a) A caravan
8. c) A high-rise building
9. a) Blow it up
10. b) WD-40

Scores

8-10: Great stuff. You must really hate pick-up trucks.
4-7: Not a total car wreck.
0-3: Lament not your lowly score, for you are a friend of the indestructible Hilux.

58

Battered cars

Though perhaps not as badly treated as the Hilux, many innocent cars have suffered at the hands of the lads. Brutal maybe, but these incidents of vehicular violence have given us some classic Top Gear moments. For instance...

1. In a race against a skydiver in the Cypriot countryside, Richard smashed up the front of what type of off-road vehicle?

a) Land Rover Discovery
b) Volvo XC90
c) Toyota Hilux
d) Porsche Cayenne

2. In a test to gauge the power of two jet engines on a 747, Richard successfully sent a Citroen 2CV and a Ford _____ flying through the air.

a) Taurus   **b)** GT
c) Mondeo   **d)** SportKa

3. In a game of car darts, which car did James and Richard manage to get closest to the caravan bullseye?

a) Volkswagen Beetle
b) Vauxhall Carlton
c) Renault Megane
d) Vauxhall Astra

4. Environmentally-friendly and emission-free, this G-Wiz had what put into it to boost its power?

a) Engines
b) People
c) Sparkplugs
d) Batteries

5. What year was the Lancia Beta Coupe Jeremy drove in Botswana?

a) 1980
b) 1981
c) 1982
d) 1983

Yeeaaaaahhhh!!

CHUG-CHUG-CHHHHUUUG!

6. In an effort to prove his point that Korean and Malaysian cars are terrible, Jeremy created a working vehicle out of what?

a) Marshmallows
b) Ice-cream sticks
c) Household appliances
d) Bicycles

7. Already broken down when James purchased it, which make of Italian supercar broke down outside of Slough, causing an embarrassing traffic jam?

a) Ferrari 308GT4
b) Maserati Merak
c) Lamborghini Urraco
d) Fiat 128

8. What '80s classic was burnt with the fiery exhaust of a drag racer?

a) Nissan Sunny
b) Volkswagen Beetle
c) Hyundai Coupe
d) Peugeot 206

JANGG

9. What type of car did the lads miraculously manage to build from scratch and drive across the finish line before The Stig?

a) Donnington Six
b) Wollesten 8
c) Caterham Seven
d) Chiswick T3

10. How many complete sideways rolls did a Ford Sierra have to complete to make it into the Guinness Book of Records?

a) 6
b) 8
c) 9
d) 12

Answers

1. d) Porsche Cayenne
2. c) Mondeo
3. b) Vauxhall Carlton
4. d) Batteries
5. b) 1981
6. c) Household appliances
7. c) Lamborghini Urraco
8. a) Nissan Sunny
9. c) Caterham Seven
10. a) 6

Scores

8-10: You like doing strange experiments with cars, don't you?

4-7: Want to play a game of car darts then?

0-3: Good old-fashioned driving on a race track is more your style.

62

/ ... his earwax tastes like Turkish Delight and that if set alight he'd burn for a thousand days. All we know is that he's called The Stig. How much do you know about our tame racing driver?

1. Complete the following. "Some say his heart..."
a) was constructed using spent nuclear fuel
b) ticks like a watch
c) is cold like the deepest, darkest recesses of space
d) holds the key to the whereabouts of the Holy Grail

2. "And that his ears..."
a) are in the shape of the Nürburgring
b) don't exist
c) aren't exactly where you'd expect them to be
d) are pretty normal

3. What was the first Stig driving when he flew off the deck of the HMS Invincible?
a) Jaguar XJS   b) Lotus Exige S
c) Roush Mustang   d) Chevrolet Corvette

4. Which make of car, the most powerful production vehicle ever featured on Top Gear (but never driven around the test track) causes The Stig to salivate from the ears whenever it is mentioned?
a) Aston Martin ZZT
b) Porsche Wildcat
c) Bugatti Veyron
d) Bowler GT3 RS

63

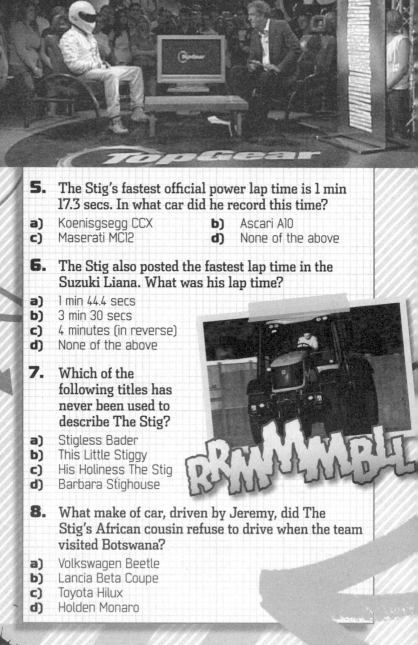

5. The Stig's fastest official power lap time is 1 min 17.3 secs. In what car did he record this time?

a) Koenisgsegg CCX
b) Ascari A10
c) Maserati MC12
d) None of the above

6. The Stig also posted the fastest lap time in the Suzuki Liana. What was his lap time?

a) 1 min 44.4 secs
b) 3 min 30 secs
c) 4 minutes (in reverse)
d) None of the above

7. Which of the following titles has never been used to describe The Stig?

a) Stigless Bader
b) This Little Stiggy
c) His Holiness The Stig
d) Barbara Stighouse

8. What make of car, driven by Jeremy, did The Stig's African cousin refuse to drive when the team visited Botswana?

a) Volkswagen Beetle
b) Lancia Beta Coupe
c) Toyota Hilux
d) Holden Monaro

9. What was the nickname given to The Stig's American cousin?

a) Chubby Chevy
b) The Spare Tyre
c) Big Stig
d) Fat Shelby

10. Where does The Stig live?

a) In a lavishly furnished apartment behind the Top Gear studio
b) In a fortress of solitude deep within the Arctic Circle
c) Clapham
d) 20,000 leagues under the sea

Answers

1. b) Ticks like a watch
2. c) Aren't exactly where you'd expect them to be.
3. a) Jaguar XJS
4. c) Bugatti Veyron
5. b) Ascari A10
6. a) 1 min 44.4 secs
7. b) This Little Stiggy
8. b) Lancia Beta Coupe
9. c) Big Stig
10. a) In a lavishly furnished apartment behind the Top Gear studio

Scores

8-10: Start choosing a colour for your suit.

4-7: Lust for speed doesn't just happen, you have to work at it. Keep trying.

0-3: Oh dear. You're much more comfortable in normal clothes, aren't you?

Race On!

As long as it's not James in the driver's seat, the lads have proven themselves to be more than capable when a race is on. From greyhounds to all-terrain skateboarders, the competitors have been a mixed bunch. How many can you remember?

1. Snooker player Ronnie O'Sullivan managed to pot 15 balls before The Stig could drive a full lap of the test track in what make of car?

a) Mercedes SL500
b) Bugatti Veyron
c) Porsche Carrera GT
d) Jaguar XK-R

2. James raced a Ford SportKa against what type of animal – and lost dismally?

a) Jaguar
b) Greyhound
c) Thoroughbred racehorse
d) Racing pigeon

How **hard** can it be?

3. Not surprisingly, James was again beaten by a professional bobsleigh team in which European country?

a) Switzerland
b) France
c) Iceland
d) Norway

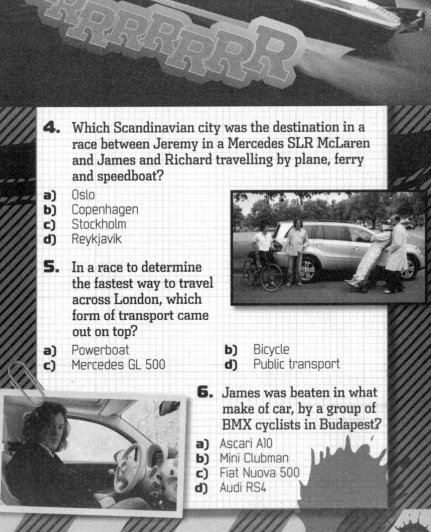

4. Which Scandinavian city was the destination in a race between Jeremy in a Mercedes SLR McLaren and James and Richard travelling by plane, ferry and speedboat?

a) Oslo
b) Copenhagen
c) Stockholm
d) Reykjavik

5. In a race to determine the fastest way to travel across London, which form of transport came out on top?

a) Powerboat
b) Bicycle
c) Mercedes GL 500
d) Public transport

6. James was beaten in what make of car, by a group of BMX cyclists in Budapest?

a) Ascari A10
b) Mini Clubman
c) Fiat Nuova 500
d) Audi RS4

7. Not even a change of scenery could improve James' fortunes. He was soundly beaten by a downhill mountain biker in which European city?

a) Barcelona
b) Madrid
c) Lisbon
d) Paris

8. The best way to beat a Mitsubishi Lancer Evo Group N rally car in a race on a muddy downhill course in Wales, is to use one of these...

a) Hanglider
b) Grass skis
c) All-terrain skateboard
d) Mountain bike

9. Richard took a turn at racing against an animal. His attempt, in a zippy MX-5, proved unsuccessful. What beat him?

a) Jaguar
b) Greyhound
c) Thoroughbred racehorse
d) Racing pigeon

10. And in order to beat a German on rollerskates, wearing a rocket jetpack on his back, you ought to consider driving one of these...

a) Aston Martin V8 Vantage
b) Ferrari 599 GTB Fiorano
c) Alfa Romeo 159
d) Mitsubishi Evo X

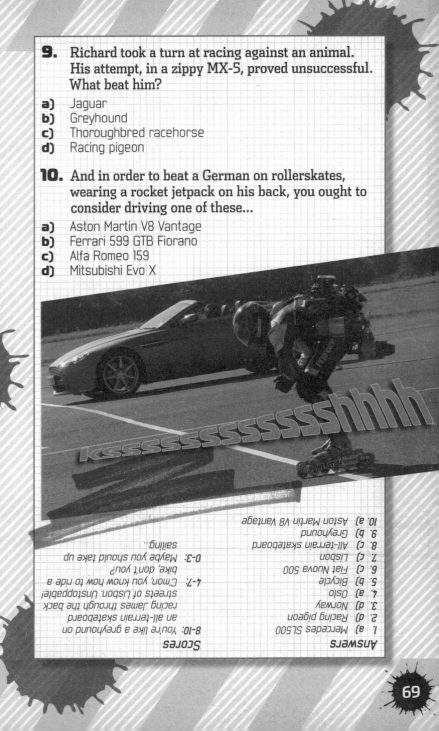

Answers

1. a) Mercedes SL500
2. d) Racing pigeon
3. d) Norway
4. a) Oslo
5. b) Bicycle
6. c) Fiat Nuova 500
7. c) Lisbon
8. c) All-terrain skateboard
9. b) Greyhound
10. a) Aston Martin V8 Vantage

Scores

8-10: You're like a greyhound on an all-terrain skateboard racing James through the back streets of Lisbon. Unstoppable!

4-7: C'mon, you know how to ride a bike, don't you?

0-3: Maybe you should take up sailing...

69

Who Said That? Part I

Actions speak louder than words. But sometimes the stuff that comes out of the lads' mouths simply can't be topped. Who said the following? Was it Jeremy, James or Richard?

1. "I am a driving God!"
   JEREMY   JAMES   RICHARD

2. "I am an alien!"
   JEREMY   JAMES   RICHARD

3. "Some say that he appears on high value stamps in Sweden, and that he can catch fish with his tongue..."
   JEREMY   JAMES   RICHARD

4. "Stop interfering, you piece of... cheap electronic tat!"
   JEREMY   JAMES   RICHARD

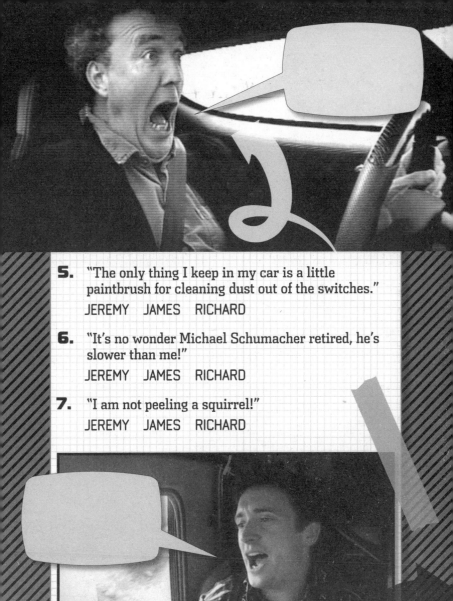

5. "The only thing I keep in my car is a little paintbrush for cleaning dust out of the switches."
JEREMY   JAMES   RICHARD

6. "It's no wonder Michael Schumacher retired, he's slower than me!"
JEREMY   JAMES   RICHARD

7. "I am not peeling a squirrel!"
JEREMY   JAMES   RICHARD

8. "I could say 'Maserati' before I could say 'Mummy'!"
   JEREMY   JAMES   RICHARD

9. "Float! OLIVER!"
   JEREMY   JAMES   RICHARD

10. "That is the delicate sound of thunder."
    JEREMY
    JAMES
    RICHARD

Answers

1. Richard
2. Jeremy
3. Jeremy
4. James
5. James
6. James
7. Richard
8. Jeremy
9. Richard
10. Jeremy

Scores

8-10: After that brilliant score, there's nothing left to say.

4-7: So you're more interested in the cars, are you? Pay attention!

0-3: It's simple. Jeremy is the tall one, Richard's the short one and James has the bad hair.

72

The USA Road Trip Challenge
True or False

The land of the brave and the home of the free. Jeremy, James and Richard met all sorts of colourful characters on their US trek. It wouldn't be a Top Gear challenge without a little excitement now, would it? Test your knowledge of the USA Road Trip Challenge.

1. The lads' journey would take them from San Francisco to New Orleans.
TRUE / FALSE

2. They first had to buy a used American car for no more than $1,000.
TRUE / FALSE

3. The Stig's American counterpart was dubbed 'Fat Stig'.
TRUE / FALSE

4. Richard's Dodge Pick-up was the slowest around the Moroso Motorsports Park.

TRUE / FALSE

5. Challenge No. 2 was was a braking test. Each of the cars had to get to 50mph and then stop before reaching a river filled with crocodiles.

TRUE / FALSE

6. One evening Jeremy went out to look for dinner and came back with a whole dead cow.

TRUE / FALSE

7. Richard painted 'Country and western is rubbish' on Jeremy's car.

TRUE / FALSE

8. The Governor of Alabama ordered local police to escort the team out of the state.

TRUE / FALSE

9. In New Orleans, the team were shocked by the devastation caused by Hurricane Bertha.

TRUE / FALSE

10. Surprisingly, Jeremy was declared the loser, as he was unable to give his car away.

TRUE / FALSE

Answers

1. *False.* Miami to New Orleans.
2. *True*
3. *False.* Though rather tubby, he was called 'Big Stig'.
4. *True*
5. *False.* The river was filled with alligators.
6. *True*
7. *True*
8. *False.* Locals convinced the team it was time to leave.
9. *False.* The devastation was caused by Hurricane Katrina.
10. *False.* James was the one who failed to find an interested motorist.

Scores

8-10: Like totally awesome score dude!

4-7: It's okay, there's some bits from this challenge you probably wanted to forget anyway. Like the cow tied to Jeremy's roof!

0-3: Did the thunderstorm wash your care for Top Gear away?

Cool Wall
Odd One Out Part II

Any luck last time? Well, don't give up. If you want to be on top of the latest and greatest machines on four wheels (never two!), you have to know what you're talking about. Agreeing with Jeremy wouldn't hurt either.

1. Vauxhall Agila, Jaguar X-Type, Citroen C-Crosser, Seat Toledo

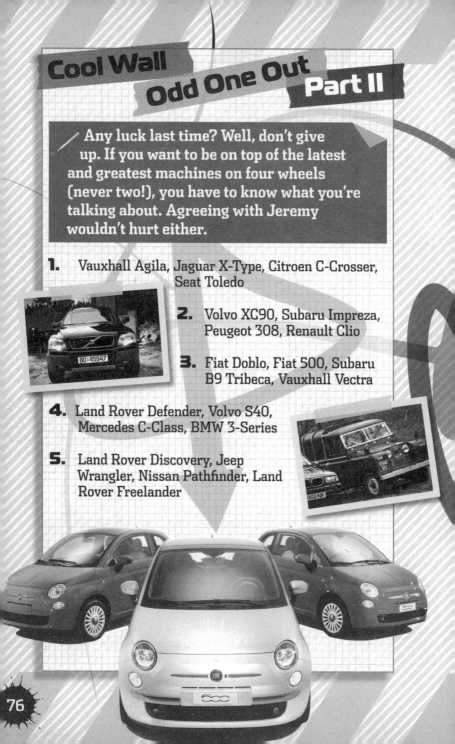

2. Volvo XC90, Subaru Impreza, Peugeot 308, Renault Clio

3. Fiat Doblo, Fiat 500, Subaru B9 Tribeca, Vauxhall Vectra

4. Land Rover Defender, Volvo S40, Mercedes C-Class, BMW 3-Series

5. Land Rover Discovery, Jeep Wrangler, Nissan Pathfinder, Land Rover Freelander

6. Subaru Impreza, Skoda Superb, Peugeot 1007, Kia Sportage

7. Toyota Landcruiser, Kia Sportage, Subaru Forester, BMW X3

8. Porsche Cayenne, Audi Q7, Volvo S60, Vauxhall Signum

9. Skoda Roomster, Fiat Panda, Suzuki Swift, Honda FR-V

10. Ferrari 308 GT4, Ferrari F40, Ferrari 599 GTB, Ferrari 512BB

Caravans

Caravans. As long as they're on the road, Jeremy, Richard and James will despise them. How many situations in this collection of classic caravan carnage can you recall?

1. A Volvo 240, at top speed, can jump over three caravans.

   TRUE / FALSE

2. And a stretch limousine will successfully jump over a wedding party without damaging a single caravan.

   TRUE / FALSE

3. In the destructive sport of Motorhome Racing, competitors must drive around a race track at high speed, towing a motorhome.

   TRUE / FALSE

4. On a caravan holiday in Dorset, Richard and Top Gear Dog were kidnapped by an elderly female fan.

TRUE / FALSE

5. Jeremy accidentally destroyed his caravan, burning it down while trying to cook chips.

TRUE / FALSE

6. After the caravan holiday film, the team received 70 complaints.

TRUE / FALSE

7. Richard and James played a game of conkers using six caravans.

TRUE / FALSE

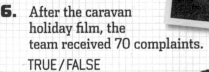

CRRUMMP

8. Even though they placed a caravan over the bullseye, neither Richard or James managed to hit the top score in a game of car darts.

TRUE / FALSE

9. The fastest way to burn a caravan is to use the jet exhaust of a drag racer.

TRUE / FALSE

10. James broke the land speed record for a caravan when he towed it behind a Mitsubishi Evo 7.

TRUE / FALSE

Answers

1. False. It can make it over two (just).
2. Obviously false. The limo managed to get over the outdoor setting but completely totalled one of the caravans.
3. False. The motorhome is an all-in-one caravan and car.
4. True
5. True
6. False. They received 150!
7. True
8. False. Richard hit the bullseye on his final 'throw'. And, of course, the caravan was destroyed.
9. True
10. False. He failed and so destroyed the caravan by dropping it from a crane.

Scores

8-10: C'mon, they're just innocent caravans! Why do you hate them so much?

4-7: Admit it, you have a soft spot for the happy little holiday homes.

0-3: Get out of the way, slow coach!

80

Who Said That? Part II

If the lads continue pulling out these gems, you'll start hearing them in the street. Or maybe not...

1. "This is a car programme. There will be no cushions, there will be no rag-rolling, no-one will sing, and at the end of the series, no one will have a recording contract."

JEREMY   JAMES   RICHARD

2. "I've won something on Top Gear!"

JEREMY   JAMES   RICHARD

3. "Atom heart mother!"

JEREMY   JAMES   RICHARD

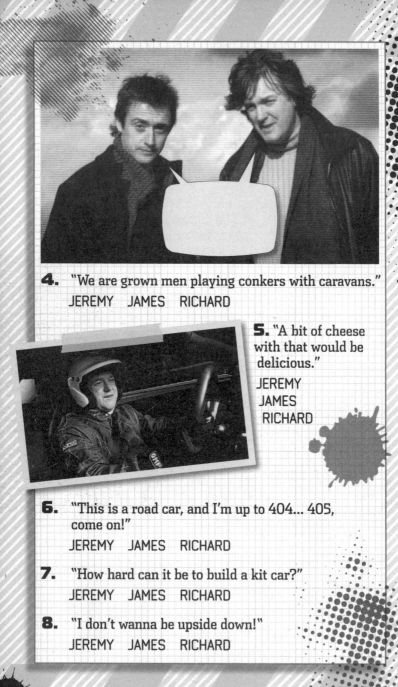

4. "We are grown men playing conkers with caravans."
JEREMY   JAMES   RICHARD

5. "A bit of cheese with that would be delicious."
JEREMY
JAMES
RICHARD

6. "This is a road car, and I'm up to 404... 405, come on!"
JEREMY   JAMES   RICHARD

7. "How hard can it be to build a kit car?"
JEREMY   JAMES   RICHARD

8. "I don't wanna be upside down!"
JEREMY   JAMES   RICHARD

9. "He's wearing cowboy boots!"

JEREMY
JAMES
RICHARD

10. "Breaker Breaker One-Nine Contact Eyeball Ten Ten 'till we do it again Captain Slow."

JEREMY   JAMES   RICHARD

Answers	
1.	Jeremy
2.	James
3.	Jeremy
4.	Richard
5.	Jeremy
6.	James
7.	James
8.	Richard
9.	Jeremy
10.	James

Scores

8-10: Considered a career as a Top Gear presenter?

4-7: If you've made it this far, you must really love Top Gear.

0-3: Whaddya want? A list of answers?

83

Chronicles of Captain Slow

True or False

What can be said about the man with an encyclopaedic knowledge of all things car-related? Quite a bit actually. Learn more about the hair with the human attached below. That is, of course, if you can sort the true statements from the fakes.

1. Set the challenge of building an amphibious vehicle, James puts a sail on a Triumph Herald. It sinks immediately.

   TRUE / FALSE

2. On his second attempt to cross the Channel, James added a centreboard keel that enabled his Triumph Herald to sail properly.

   TRUE / FALSE

I'm going to fit it with a mast and some sails. **How brilliant is that?**

3. Though his nickname is Captain Slow, James' one strength on the road is navigating.

TRUE / FALSE

4. He is a qualified light aircraft pilot.

TRUE / FALSE

5. And he can play the piano and trombone.

TRUE / FALSE

6. On the American Challenge, James had 'NASCAR sucks' painted on the side of his car by Jeremy.

TRUE / FALSE

7. James is given the task of driving singer Lemar to the BRIT Awards, but gets lost and never arrives.

TRUE / FALSE

KA-POWWW

8. Under the tutelage of racing legend Sir Jackie Stewart, Captain Slow manages to reduce his lap time of the Oulton Park circuit in a TVR Tuscan by 20 seconds.

TRUE / FALSE

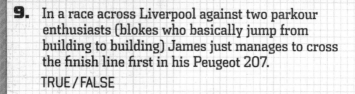

9. In a race across Liverpool against two parkour enthusiasts (blokes who basically jump from building to building) James just manages to cross the finish line first in his Peugeot 207.

TRUE / FALSE

10. James had little luck when given the opportunity to drive the Bugatti Veyron at maximum speed. Even though he was on a test track, James couldn't quite reach the mark, blaming the wet road and high winds.

TRUE / FALSE

Answers

1. *False.* This was one challenge James actually won.
2. *False.* Don't be ridiculous. It sank on the first attempt.
3. *False.* His sense of direction is even worse than his lap times.
4. *True.* Though, when we last checked he couldn't fly at night.
5. *False.* He plays the piano and flute.
6. *True.*
7. *True.* Poor Lemar.
8. *True.* Amazing but true.
9. *False.* Same old story – Captain Slow got lost.
10. *False.* For a brief time, Captain Slow was faster than anything else on the road.

Scores

8-10: Well done! Do you have lustrous locks as well?

4-7: Like the Captain himself, a little slow off the mark.

0-3: I think you need to watch more Top Gear.

Stupidly Hard Quiz!

Yeah okay, the questions up to now haven't been all that easy, but you've reached this far, haven't you? Well then, these 20 Stupidly Hard Questions should be about as easy as controlling a Lotus Exige on a wet track. Get to it!

1. Which female celebrity, faced disqualification after failing to properly complete some corners?

a) Billie Piper
b) Davina McCall
c) Joanna Lumley
d) Jodie Kidd

2. What is Top Gear's greatest ever driving song as voted by viewers?

a) 'Danger Zone' by Kenny Loggins
b) 'I Should Be So Lucky' by Kylie Minogue
c) 'Get Ready To Wiggle' by The Wiggles
d) 'Don't Stop Me Now' by Queen

3. Which singer broke the wheel off the Liana during his test drive?

SKREEEEEEEEEEEE

a) Trevor Eve
b) Jay Kay
c) Vinnie Jones
d) Lionel Richie

VARROOOOMMM

4. What car did Jeremy drive around the Top Gear test track until it ran out of petrol?

a) Koenigsegg CCX
b) Ford GT
c) Ascari A10
d) Volvo 240

5. What car did Jeremy dub 'an Enzo in drag'?

a) Ferrari Enzo
b) Pagani Zonda F
c) Aston Martin DBS
d) Maserati MC12

6. In a race against a Eurofighter Typhoon, Richard, driving a Bugatti Veyron, is beaten by how many seconds?

a) 2
b) 4
c) 7
d) 40

7. As accompaniment to Richard's announcement that he was shipping 'Oliver' the Opel Kadett home to England, James played what tune on his portable keyboard?

a) 'Canon in D' by Johann Pachelbel
b) 'Some Enchanted Evening' by Rodgers and Hammerstein
c) 'I Adore Mi Amor' by Color Me Badd
d) 'Romeo and Juliet Theme' by Nino Rota

8. What was the nationality of the turbo-powered roller skater beaten by Richard in an Aston Martin V8 Vantage?

a) Australian
b) Swiss
c) German
d) British

9. How many motorcycles can a double-decker bus jump over?

a) 2
b) 3
c) 7
d) 9

10. And how many bouncy castles can an ice cream van jump over?

a) 2
b) 3
c) 4
d) None

11. Which England rugby star posted a lap time of 1 min 47.4 secs in the Lacetti?

a) Jonny Wilkinson
b) Olly Barkley
c) Lawrence Dallaglio
d) Mark Regan

12. Which country launched its own version of Top Gear in 2008?

a) China
b) United States
c) Australia
d) France

13. What time did singer James Blunt post, on a suitably wet track?

a) 1 min 48.3 secs
b) 1 min 49 secs
c) 1 min 54.2 secs
d) Did not finish

14. Who is the fastest F1 star around the Top Gear test track?

a) Nigel Mansell
b) Jenson Button
c) Lewis Hamilton
d) Damon Hill

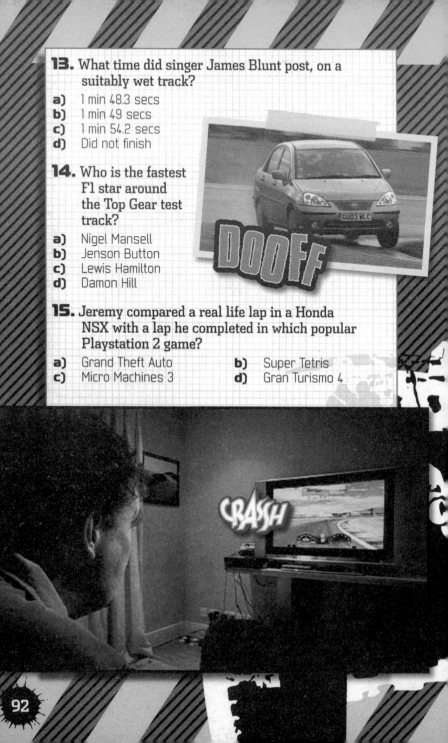

15. Jeremy compared a real life lap in a Honda NSX with a lap he completed in which popular Playstation 2 game?

a) Grand Theft Auto
b) Super Tetris
c) Micro Machines 3
d) Gran Turismo 4

VRROOOMM

16. What did Jeremy do his best to avoid on the British army's Salisbury Plain?

a) Apache Attack Chopper
b) Austin-Healey Sprite
c) Challenger 2 Tank
d) Rocket-powered German on roller skates

17. Which car took out Car of the Year in 2006?

a) Mercedes-Benz McLaren
b) Caterham 7 kit car
c) Lamborghini Gallardo Spyder
d) Subaru Legacy Outback

18. And what won the year before?

a) Bugatti Veyron
b) Volkswagen Golf
c) Aston Martin DB5
d) Ford GT

SCREEEECH!

19. Dame Ellen MacArthur set the fastest lap time of any celebrity in the Liana. What else is she known for?

a) Speed skating   **b)** Sailing
c) Cooking   **d)** Acting

20. Which car was the named the worst of 2007?

a) Mini Clubman
b) Suzuki Swift
c) G-Wiz
d) Hyundai Accent

Answers

1. a) Billie Piper
2. d) 'Don't Stop Me Now' by Queen
3. d) Lionel Richie
4. b) Ford GT
5. d) Maserati MC12
6. a) Two
7. d) 'Romeo and Juliet Theme' by Nino Rota
8. c) German
9. b) 3 (and crashed into eleven others)
10. d) None (Spectacular, but pathetic)
11. c) Lawrence Dallaglio
12. c) Australia
13. a) 1 min 48.3 secs
14. e) Nigel Mansell
15. d) Gran Turismo 4
16. c) Challenger 2 Tank
17. c) Lamborghini Gallardo Spyder
18. a) Bugatti Veyron
19. b) Sailing
20. c) G-Wiz

Scores

15-20: If a Porsche GT was the prize for top marks in this section, you'd win it. Unfortunately for you, there is no prize.

7-14: Considering these were the Stupidly Hard Questions, you should still be pleased with your score. Actually, on second thoughts, it was pretty rubbish.

0-6: Look on the bright side. You can always turn to the start of the book and do it all over again.

94